# Reading STREET

## GEORGIA

## Program Authors

Peter Afflerbach

Camille Blachowicz

Candy Dawson Boyd

Wendy Cheyney

Connie Juel

Edward Kame'enui

Donald Leu

Jeanne Paratore

P. David Pearson

Sam Sebesta

Deborah Simmons

Sharon Vaughn

Susan Watts-Taffe

Karen Kring Wixson

PEARSON

Scott Foresman

**Editorial Offices:** Glenview, Illinois • Parsippany, New Jersey • New York, New York
**Sales Offices:** Boston, Massachusetts • Duluth, Georgia • Glenview, Illinois
Coppell, Texas • Sacramento, California • Mesa, Arizona

*We dedicate Reading Street to*
*Peter Jovanovich.*

*His wisdom, courage,*
*and passion for education*
*are an inspiration to us all.*

**About the Cover Artist**
Daniel Moreton lives in New York City, where he uses his computer to create illustrations for books. When he is not working, Daniel enjoys cooking, watching movies, and traveling. On a trip to Mexico, Daniel was inspired by all of the bright colors around him. He likes to use those colors in his art.

ISBN-13: 978-0-328-42202-9
ISBN-10:    0-328-42202-9

 2 3 4 5 6 7 8 9 10 V063 17 16 15 14 13 12 11 10 09

CC:1

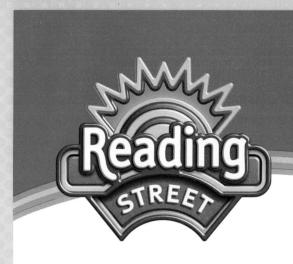

Dear Georgia Reader,

As you continue your trip down *Scott Foresman Reading Street,* you will learn about yourself and others. And, you will improve your reading skills as you travel along!

What changes have you experienced as you have grown? What changes have you noticed in the world around you? The stories and articles in this book are all about changes.

Take time to enjoy yourself and the changes all around you as you continue along *Scott Foresman Reading Street!*

Sincerely,
The Authors

# Changes

## What is changing in our world?

### Growing and Changing

# Changes in Nature

# Changes

## What is changing in our world?

## An Egg Is an Egg
A boy describes changes in our world.

**REALISTIC FICTION**

*connect to* **SCIENCE**

## Ruby in Her Own Time
A young duckling grows and learns.

**ANIMAL FANTASY**

*connect to* **SOCIAL STUDIES**

## Jan's New Home
Moving is a difficult change for Jan.

**REALISTIC FICTION**

*connect to* **SOCIAL STUDIES**

## Frog and Toad Together
Toad sees his garden grow and change.

**ANIMAL FANTASY**

*connect to* **SCIENCE**

## I'm a Caterpillar
A caterpillar changes to a butterfly.

**NARRATIVE NONFICTION**

*connect to* **SCIENCE**

## Where Are My Animal Friends?
The seasons bring many changes to the forest.

**PLAY**

*connect to* **SCIENCE**

# Let's Talk About
# Growing and Changing

# Words to Read

| things |
| --- |
| always |
| day |
| become |
| nothing |
| stays |
| everything |

# Read the Words

Some things always change.
They change from day to day.
Children get bigger. Seeds become
plants. Nothing stays the same.
Everything changes.

**Genre: Realistic Fiction**
Realistic fiction has
characters that act like real
people. In *An Egg Is an Egg*,
you will read about changes
that take place in our world.

# An Egg Is an Egg

## by Nicki Weiss

When is an egg not an egg?

An egg is an egg until it hatches.
And then it is a chick.

A branch is a branch until it breaks.
And then it is a stick.

Nothing stays the same.
Everything can change.

A seed is a seed until it is sown.
And then it is a flower.

A block is a block until there are many.
And then they become a tower.

Nothing stays the same.
Everything can change.

Water is water until it is brewed.
And then it becomes tea.

You are you until I come.
And then you become "we."

Nothing stays the same.
Everything can change.

The yard is green until it snows.
And then it becomes white.

Day is day until sunset.
And then it is the night.

Nothing stays the same.
Everything can change.

This baby was a baby until he grew.
And now he is a boy.

But you can always be a baby.
You will always be my baby. . . .

Some things stay the same.
Some things never change.

# Think and Share

**Talk About It** Which change in *An Egg Is an Egg* is your favorite? Tell about it.

**1.** Use the pictures below to retell the story.
Retell

**2.** Choose a pair of pictures from the story. How are they alike and different?
Compare/Contrast

**3.** Did you predict how the yard would change? What helped you? Predict

**Look Back and Write** Look back at page 25. Write about one thing that does not change.

# Nicki Weiss

Nicki Weiss is an artist, a writer, and a teacher. Her books are about friends, family love, and changes in life.

Ms. Weiss lives in New York City. She wrote lots of books. Then she decided to become a schoolteacher. Now she teaches reading and art. She still writes books when she has the time.

**Read more books by Nicki Weiss.**

# Nothing Fits!

by Rena Moran

illustrated by Mary Bono

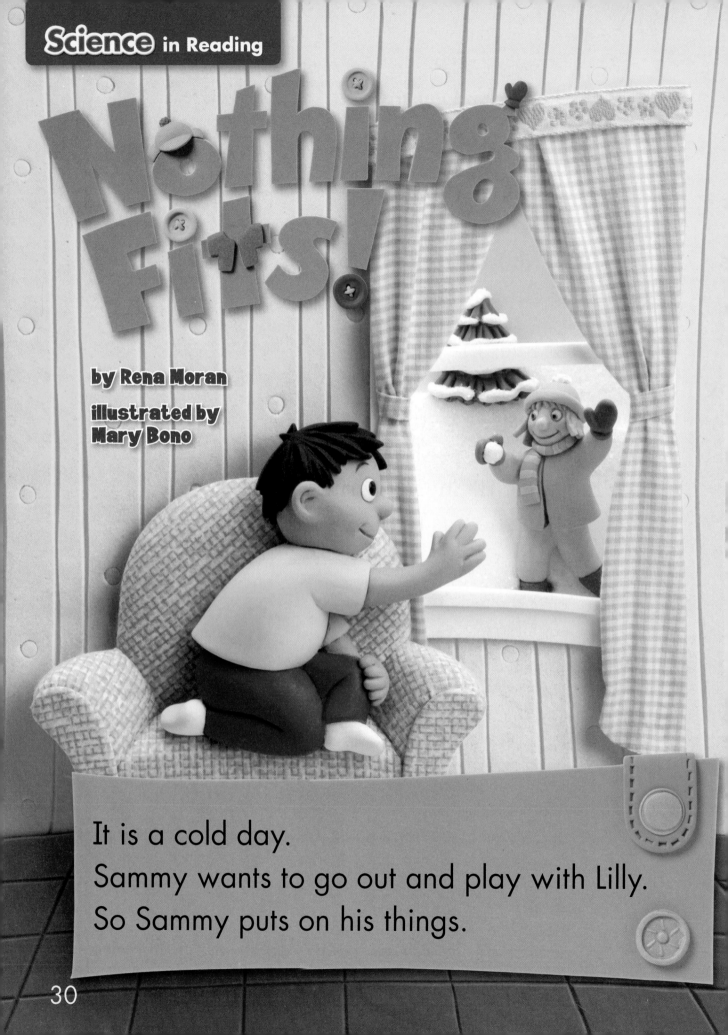

It is a cold day.

Sammy wants to go out and play with Lilly.

So Sammy puts on his things.

Sammy looks silly!
Nothing fits him.
Everything is too small.
Sammy grew.

Dad has new things for Sammy.
He must try them on.
Everything fits!
Sammy will not have to stay inside.

Sammy will keep growing.
He will become a big boy.
But he will always be Sammy.

# Write Now

## Writing and Grammar

## Steps

### Prompt

*An Egg Is an Egg* shows that almost everything changes. Think about how an egg changes to become a chicken. Now write steps that tell what happens. Put the steps in order.

**Writing Trait**

Capital letters and end marks are sentence **conventions.**

**Student Model**

**Steps are in order, from first to last.**

**Each sentence tells one step.**

**Writer follows sentence <u>conventions</u>.**

A hen lays an egg.

The hen sits on the egg.

The egg cracks in two.

A chick leaves the egg.

The chick grows into a chicken.

34

**GEORGIA Writing**
For weekly writing in CRCT format, see the
*Georgia Weekly CRCT Workbook*, pages 77–80.

GEORGIA · Writing

## Writer's Checklist

✓ **Ideas** Are all sentences about the topic?

✓ **Organization** Are steps in the right order?

✓ **Style** Does each sentence tell about one step?

✓ **Conventions** Does every sentence begin with a capital letter and end with a period?

# Grammar

## Action Verbs

A **verb** can tell what someone or something does.

Mom **plants** seeds.
The seeds **grow.**

The word **plants** tells what Mom does.
The word **grow** tells what the seeds do.

· · · · · · · · · · · · · · · · · · · · · · · · · ·

Look at the steps. Write the action verbs in the sentences.

**GEORGIA**
**Performance Standards** **ELA1W1I.** Uses appropriate end punctuation (period and question mark) and correct
capitalization of initial words and common proper nouns (e.g., personal names, months). (Also **ELA1W1.**)

35

# Let's Talk About
## Growing and Changing

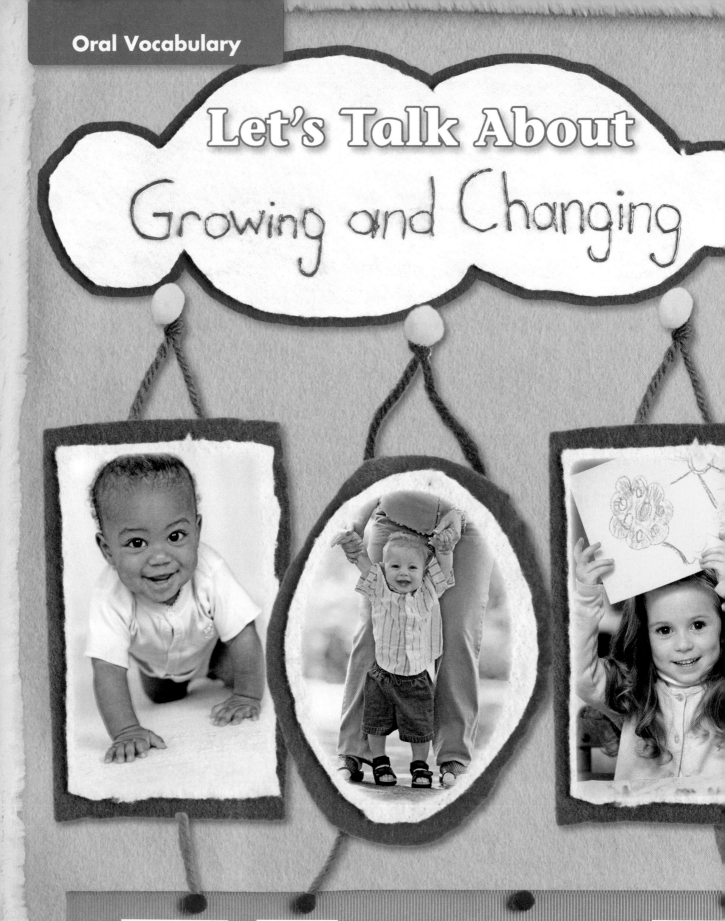

6 months  1 year    2 years    3 yea

36

4 years

5 years

6 years

# Words to Read

| |
|---|
| **ever** |
| **sure** |
| **were** |
| **enough** |
| **every** |
| **any** |
| **own** |

# Read the Words

"Have you ever seen this cute duck family in the pond?" asked Ben.

"Sure," said Jill. "They were here last week. I had seeds to feed them then, but not enough for every little duck. Now I don't have any seeds."

"They will have to get their own food," said Ben.

**Genre: Animal Fantasy**
An animal fantasy is a story with animal characters that talk. Next you will read about a growing duck family.

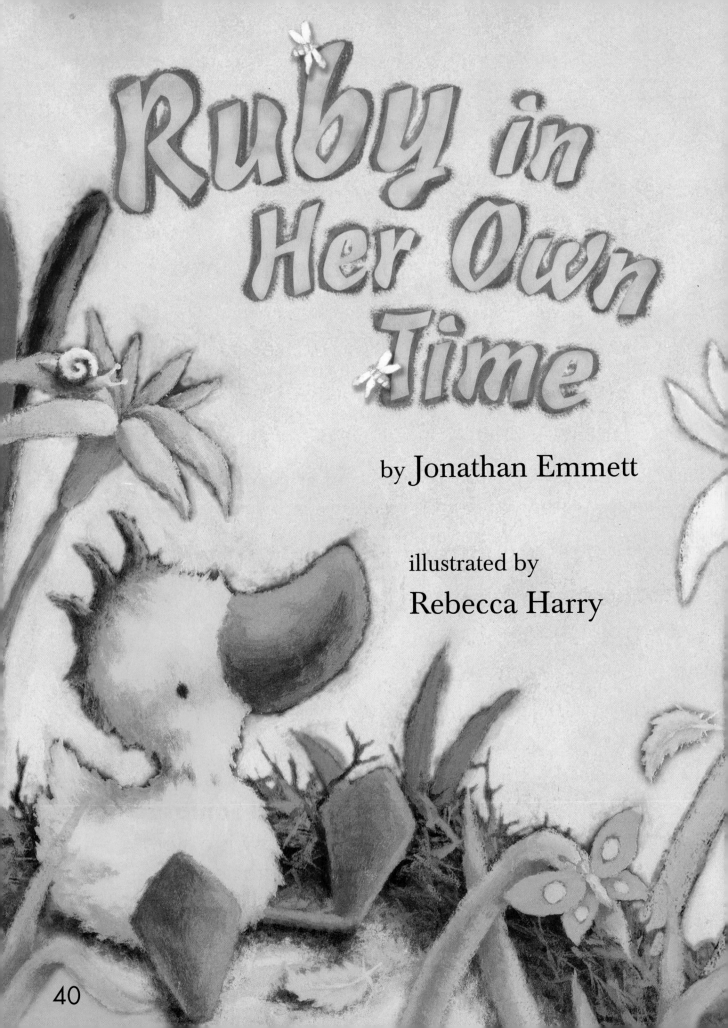

# Ruby in Her Own Time

by Jonathan Emmett

illustrated by Rebecca Harry

**What will Ruby
learn as she grows?**

41

Once upon a time upon a nest
beside a lake, there lived two ducks—
a mother duck and a father duck.

There were five eggs in the
nest. Mother Duck sat upon the
nest, all day and all night . . .

through howling wind and driving rain,
looking after the eggs—all five of them.

Then, one bright morning,
the eggs began to hatch.

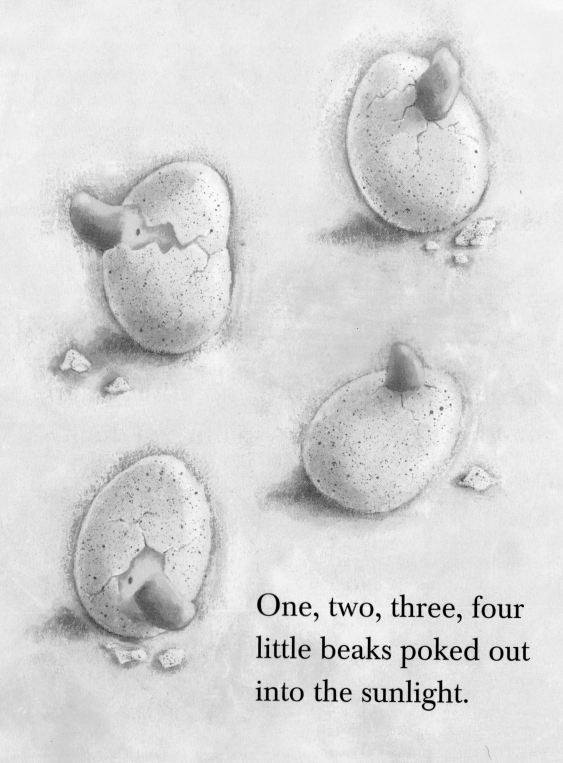

One, two, three, four
little beaks poked out
into the sunlight.

One, two, three, four little ducklings
shook their feathers in the breeze.

"We'll call them Rufus, Rory, Rosie,
and Rebecca," said Father Duck.
And Mother Duck agreed.

But the fifth egg did nothing.
"Will it ever hatch?" said Father Duck.

"It will," said Mother Duck,
"in its own time."

And–
sure enough–
it did.

"She's very small," said Father Duck.
"What shall we call her?"

"We'll call her Ruby," said Mother Duck,
"because she's small and precious."

Rufus, Rory, Rosie, and Rebecca
ate whatever they were given.
They ate anything and everything.

But Ruby ate nothing.

"Will she ever eat?" said Father Duck.

"She will," said Mother
Duck, "in her own time."

And–
sure enough–
she did.

Rufus, Rory, Rosie, and Rebecca swam off whenever they were able.

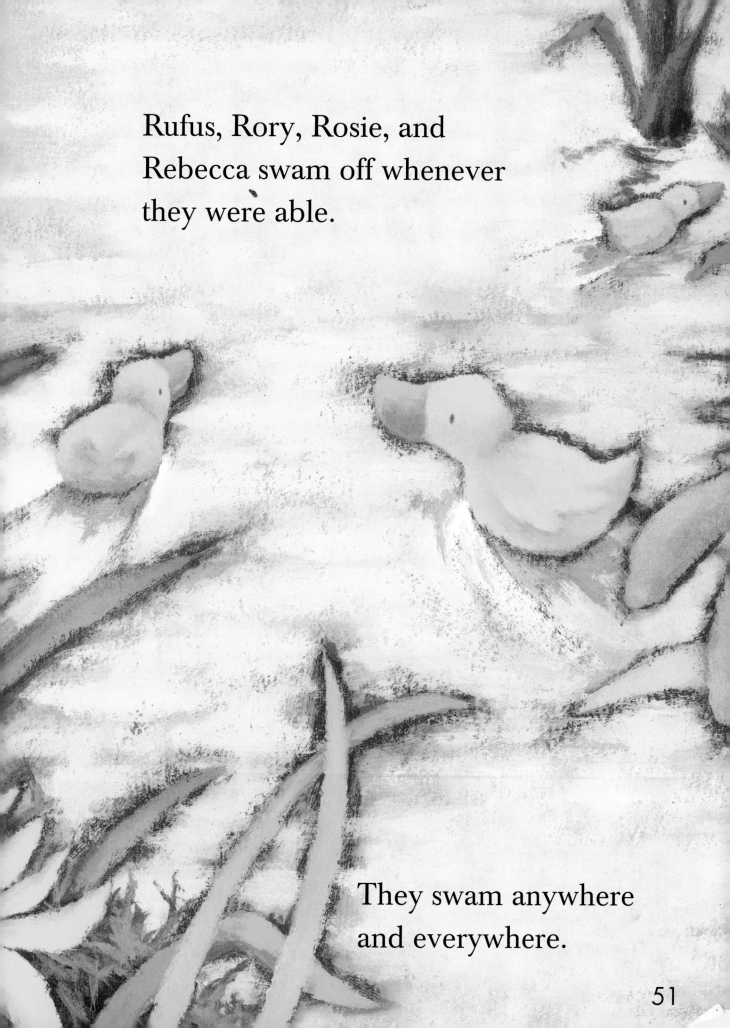

They swam anywhere and everywhere.

But Ruby swam nowhere.

"Will she ever swim?" said Father Duck.

"She will," said Mother Duck,
"in her own time."

And–
sure enough–
she did.

Rufus, Rory, Rosie, and
Rebecca grew bigger.

And Ruby grew bigger too.
Her feathers grew out, and her
wings grew broad and beautiful.

And when Rufus, Rory, Rosie,
and Rebecca began to fly . . .

Ruby flew too!

Rufus, Rory, Rosie, and Rebecca flew far and wide. They flew out across the water. They flew up among the trees.

But Ruby flew farther
and wider. She flew out
beyond the water.

She flew up above
the trees.

56

She flew anywhere and everywhere.
She stretched out her beautiful wings
and soared high among the clouds.

Mother Duck and Father Duck watched
Ruby flying off into the distance.

"Will she ever come back?"
said Mother Duck.

"She will," said Father
Duck, "in her own time."

And—
sure enough—
she did.

# Think and Share

**Talk About It** What surprised you at the end of the story? Tell about it.

**1.** Use the pictures below to retell the order in which things happen in this story. Retell

**2.** What do you think was the most exciting part of this story? Plot

**3.** Sum up how Ruby grew and changed.
Summarize

**Look Back and Write** Look back at page 47. Why did Mother Duck name her baby duck *Ruby?* Write about it.

# Jonathan Emmett

Jonathan Emmett got the idea for this story while jogging around a lake one morning. He saw a swan's nest, and the words "Once upon a time, upon a nest" popped into his head. He changed the swans to ducks, "and the story grew from there."

Mr. Emmett lives in England with his wife and two children.

**Read more books by Jonathan Emmett.**

63

# I'm Growing

When I was a baby, I couldn't do anything on my own. Mom and Dad sure were a big help!

Then, every day I could do new things. Look at what things I could do. Here's my list.

| What I could do | When I did it |
| --- | --- |
| Walk | 1 year |
| Talk | 2 years |
| Sing a song | 3 years |
| Brush teeth | 4 years |
| Play catch with a mitt | 5 years |
| Ride a two-wheel bike | 6 years |

When I am old enough, I could fly a plane! Do you ever think of what you will do?

## List

### Prompt

In *Ruby in Her Own Time,* a baby duck grows up.
Think about things Ruby does as she grows up.
Now write a list of these things using numbered sentences.

**Writing Trait**

A list of sentences can show events in **order.**

**Student Model**

**Title tells what list is about.**

Things Ruby Does

1. Ruby eats.

**Details support title.**

2. Ruby swims in the water.

3. Ruby soars in the sky.

4. Ruby comes back.

**Numbers show <u>order</u> of items in list.**

## Writer's Checklist

✓ **Ideas** Are all sentences about the topic?

✓ **Organization** Are sentences written in a list?

✓ **Style** Does each detail tell about an action?

✓ **Conventions** Does every sentence begin with a capital letter and end with a period?

# Grammar

## Verbs That Add -s

A **verb** can tell what one person, animal, or thing does. Add an **-s** to show what is being done now.

Ruby **swims** in the pond.

Ruby is one duck, so we add **-s** to **swim.**

• • • • • • • • • • • • • • • • • • • • • • • • • •

Look at the sentences in the list. Write the verbs. What letter is at the end of each verb? Why is that letter there?

**GEORGIA**
**Performance Standards** **ELA1W1e.** Writes in complete sentences with correct subject-verb agreement.
(Also **ELA1W1.**)
GPS

67

# Let's Talk About
# Growing and Changing

# Words to Read

| very |
| --- |
| car |
| away |
| our |
| house |
| school |
| friends |

# Read the Words

Jan was very sad. As her family drove off in the car, she said, "I don't want to go away. I like our house. I like my school and my friends. Let's stay here."

**Genre: Realistic Fiction**
Realistic fiction is a made-up story about things that could really happen. The next story is about a girl who must move to a new home.

# Jan's New Home

by Angela Shelf Medearis

illustrated by Don Tate

## What will change when Jan moves to a new home?

Jan and her family must move away.
Jan is sad. She wants to stay.

Our house, our school,
our friends will change.
But Jan wishes everything
could stay the same.

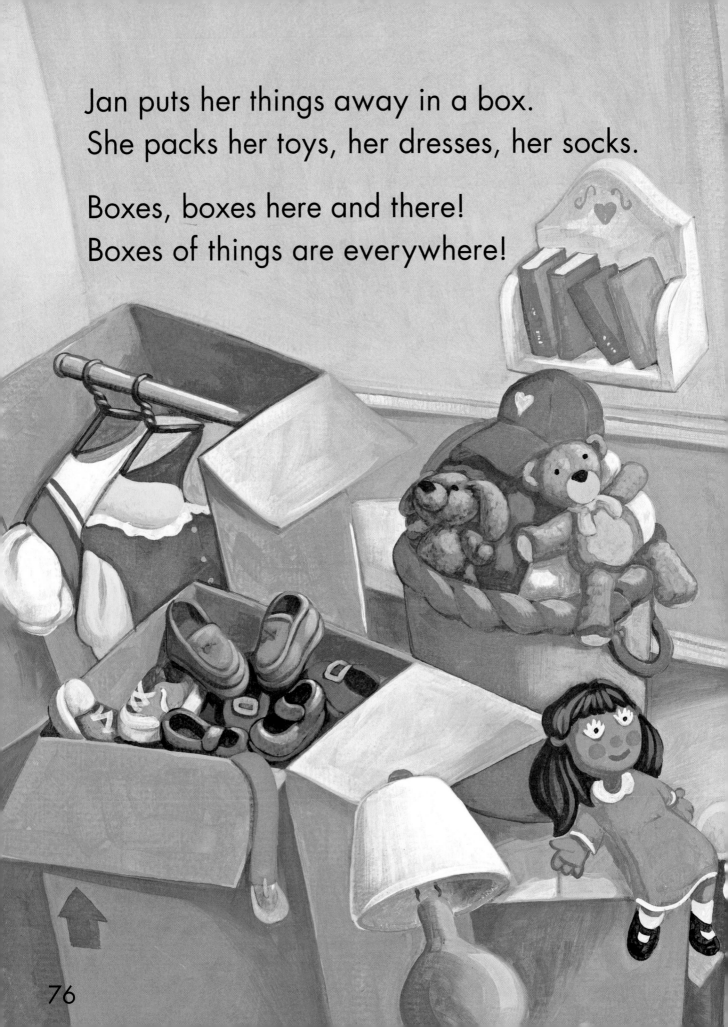

Jan puts her things away in a box.
She packs her toys, her dresses, her socks.

Boxes, boxes here and there!
Boxes of things are everywhere!

Jan packs her things, big and small,
and takes her stuff down from the wall.

Boxes, boxes here and there!
Boxes, boxes everywhere!

Our time in this home is at an end.
Time for a new house, new school,
new friends.

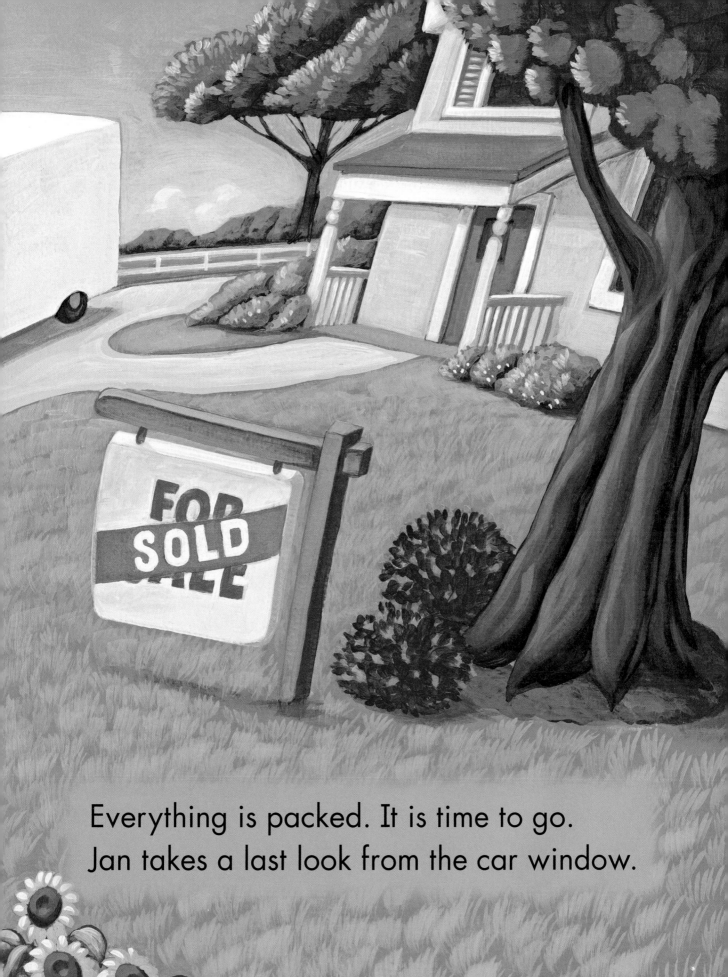

Everything is packed. It is time to go.
Jan takes a last look from the car window.

She sees horses, sheep, and lots of trees,
beautiful flowers and buzzing bees.

They stop for a picnic on the way.
Jan and her family eat and play.
It's a beautiful day with lots of sun.
Jan feels good. This trip is fun!

Cars and buses are everywhere.
People rush here, and people rush there.

There are lots of stores and very tall towers.
No more horses or tall yellow flowers.

Time for bed.
We have come a long way.
This is our new home.
We are here to stay.

New house, new school, and lots of change.
But Jan's little bed is still the same.
Some things are new. Some things change.
But the very best things are still the same.

# Think and Share

**Talk About It** What would you miss most if you were to move away from your home?

**1.** Use the pictures below to retell the story. Retell

**2.** What big lesson did Jan learn about change? Theme

**3.** Did anything confuse you as you read? What did you do about it? How did that help? Monitor/Fix Up

**Look Back and Write** Look back at pages 82–83. How is Jan's new neighborhood different from her old one?

## Meet the Author

# Angela Shelf Medearis

Angela Medearis has moved to a new home many times. She says, "My father was in the Air Force. We moved almost every year!"

Ms. Medearis says to get better at reading, read as much as you can. "Put a book in the car. Keep a book in your backpack so you will always have something fun to do!"

**Read more books by Angela Shelf Medearis.**

# A Letter from Jan

Dear Hope,

I was sad when we drove away in our car. I liked our old house very much. But now I like my new home! We still have lots of boxes in the house.

I met more friends at school. They are very nice.

I hope you will come to see me.

Your friend,
Jan

This is for you.
It is my new home.

# Write Now

## Writing and Grammar

**Read Together**

## Greeting Card

### Prompt

In *Jan's New Home,* Jan moves to a new city.
Think about how you would welcome Jan to your class.
Now write a greeting card telling Jan about your class.

**Writing Trait**

A greeting card has a friendly **voice.**

---

**Student Model**

**First line shows friendly <u>voice.</u>**

**Sentence gives good picture.**

**Verbs tell what happens in class.**

Welcome to our class, Jan!
Each day we read and
write in our journals. Our
frisky gerbils Al and Max
run on the wheel. Speakers
tell about their jobs.
Susan Bloom

90

GEORGIA • Writing

GEORGIA Writing
For weekly writing in CRCT format, see the
*Georgia Weekly CRCT Workbook*, pages 93–96.

## Writer's Checklist

- ✓ **Ideas** Do all sentences stick to the topic?
- ✓ **Organization** Are ideas in an order that makes sense?
- ✓ **Style** Do words make the card sound friendly?
- ✓ **Conventions** Are all words spelled correctly?

# Grammar

## Verbs That Do Not Add -s

Do not add **-s** to a verb that tells what two or more people, animals, or things do now.

Jan and her mother **pack** boxes.

Two people are packing, so we do not add **-s** to **pack.**

• • • • • • • • • • • • • • • • • • • • • • • • • •

Look at the greeting card to Jan. Write the verbs that tell what happens in class. Why don't the verbs end in **-s?**

GEORGIA
**Performance Standards** **ELA1W1e.** Writes in complete sentences with correct subject-verb agreement.
(Also **ELA1W1b.**)

91

Let's Talk About

# Changes in Nature

93

# Words to Read

| afraid |
| --- |
| read |
| soon |
| again |
| how |
| few |

## Read the Words

Frog was afraid. Toad read to him. Soon Frog went to sleep again.

"Now how can I get to sleep?" asked Toad. "I will read a few pages to myself."

Frog and Toad
Together
The Garden

**Genre: Animal Fantasy**

In an animal fantasy, animals say and do things that people might say and do. Next you will read about two friends, Frog and Toad, who act very much like people.

# Frog and Toad Together

by Arnold Lobel

## The Garden

What do seeds need to grow?

Frog was in his garden.
Toad came walking by.

"What a fine garden you have, Frog,"
he said.

"Yes," said Frog. "It is very nice,
but it was hard work."

"I wish I had a garden," said Toad.

"Here are some flower seeds.
Plant them in the ground," said Frog,
"and soon you will have a garden."

"How soon?" asked Toad.

"Quite soon," said Frog.

Toad ran home.
He planted the flower seeds.

"Now seeds," said Toad, "start growing."

Toad walked up and down a few times.
The seeds did not start to grow.

Toad put his head close to
the ground and said loudly,

"Now seeds,
start growing!"

Toad looked at the ground again.
The seeds did not start to grow.

Toad put his head very close
to the ground and shouted,

# "NOW SEEDS, START GROWING!"

Frog came running up the path.
"What is all this noise?" he asked.

"My seeds will not grow," said Toad.

"You are shouting too much," said Frog.
"These poor seeds are afraid to grow."

"My seeds are afraid to grow?"
asked Toad.

"Of course," said Frog.
"Leave them alone for a few days.
Let the sun shine on them,
let the rain fall on them.
Soon your seeds will start to grow."

That night Toad looked out of his window.

"Drat!" said Toad. "My seeds have not started to grow. They must be afraid of the dark." Toad went out to his garden with some candles.

"I will read the seeds a story,"
said Toad. "Then they will not be afraid."

Toad read a long story to his seeds.

All the next day Toad
sang songs to his seeds.

And all the next day Toad read poems to his seeds.

And all the next day Toad played music for his seeds.

Toad looked at the ground.
The seeds still did not start to grow.

"What shall I do?" cried Toad.
"These must be the most frightened
seeds in the whole world!"

Then Toad felt very tired, and he fell asleep.

"Toad, Toad, wake up," said Frog.
"Look at your garden!"

Toad looked at his garden.

Little green plants were coming
up out of the ground.

"At last," shouted Toad, "my seeds
have stopped being afraid to grow!"

"And now you will have a nice garden too," said Frog.

"Yes," said Toad, "but you were right, Frog. It was very hard work."

# Think and Share

**Talk About It** What was the funniest thing Toad did to get his seeds to grow? Read that part out loud.

**1.** Use the pictures below to retell the story.
   Retell

**2.** What did you think about the story's ending? Tell about it. Plot

**3.** What picture came to your mind when you read about Toad playing music for his plants? How did that help you? Visualize

**Look Back and Write** Look back at page 104. What advice does Frog give to Toad?

## Meet the Author and Illustrator
# Arnold Lobel

When Arnold Lobel first wrote about Frog and Toad, there were not many books for beginning readers that were fun to read. Mr. Lobel used easy words, and children love those good friends Frog and Toad!

As a boy, Mr. Lobel liked to draw silly animal pictures for his friends. When he grew up, he wrote and illustrated almost 100 books!

**Read more stories about Frog and Toad.**

# Growing Plants

Do not be afraid to start a garden.
It is not hard. Read how.

**1.** Plant a few seeds.

**2.** Let the sun shine on them.

**3.** Water the seeds again and again.

Soon you will be growing
large plants.

**1.**

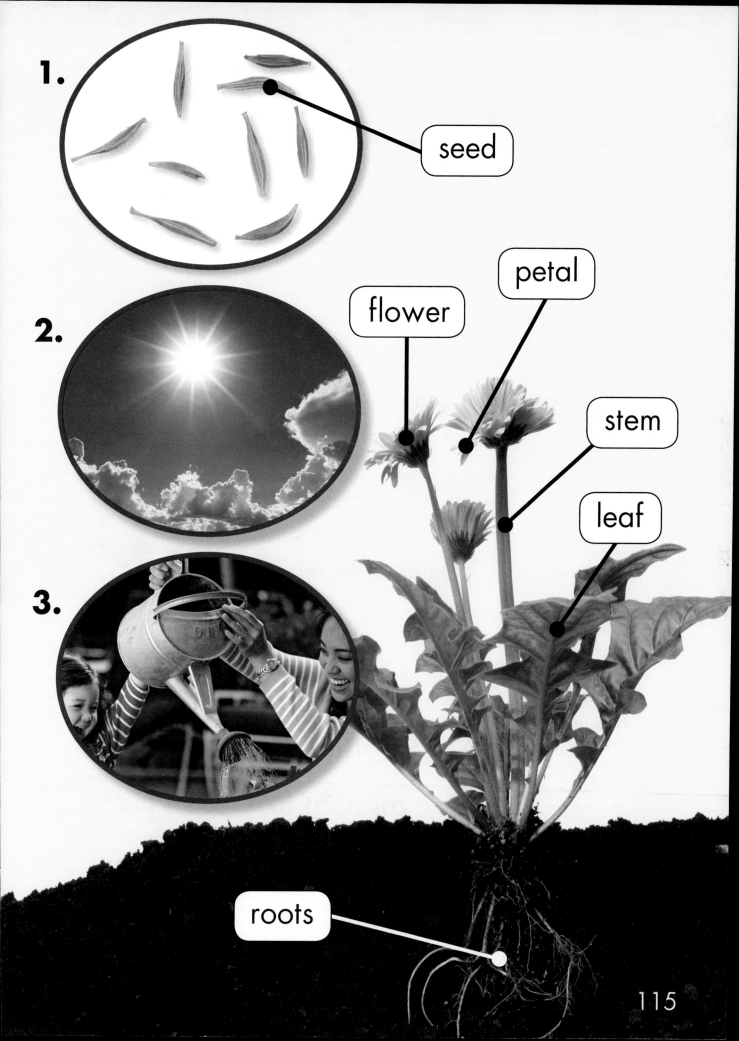

seed

petal

flower

stem

**2.**

leaf

**3.**

roots

## Poem

### Prompt

*Frog and Toad Together* tells about planting seeds to grow flowers in gardens.

Think about things that grow— seeds, flowers, or gardens. Now write a poem about one of these things.

**Writing Trait**

**Choose words** that rhyme for your poem.

**Student Model**

**Poem tells story.**

**Events are told in time order.**

Word choice includes rhyming words.

### Jen's Garden

Jen wanted some flowers,

So she planted some seeds.

Two months later, Jen picks

All the flowers she needs!

GEORGIA · Writing

GEORGIA Writing
For weekly writing in CRCT format, see the
*Georgia Weekly CRCT Workbook*, pages 101–104.

## Writer's Checklist

☑ **Ideas** Does the poem tell about one idea?

☑ **Organization** Are sentences written in poem form?

☑ **Style** Does the poem have rhyming words?

☑ **Conventions** Does each line begin with a capital letter?

# Grammar

## Verbs for Now and the Past

Verbs can tell what happens now. Verbs can tell what happened in the past. Some verbs that tell about the past end with **-ed.**

Toad **plants** seeds. (now)

Toad **planted** seeds. (past)

· · · · · · · · · · · · · · · · · · · · · · · · · · · · · · · ·

Look at the poem. Write the verbs that tell about the past in one list. Write the verbs that tell about now in another list.

**GEORGIA**
**Performance Standards** **ELA1W1.** The student begins to demonstrate competency in the writing process.
**GPS** (Also **ELA1W1e.**)

117

# Let's Talk About
# Changes in Nature

# Words to Read

| |
|---|
| know |
| done |
| push |
| wait |
| visit |

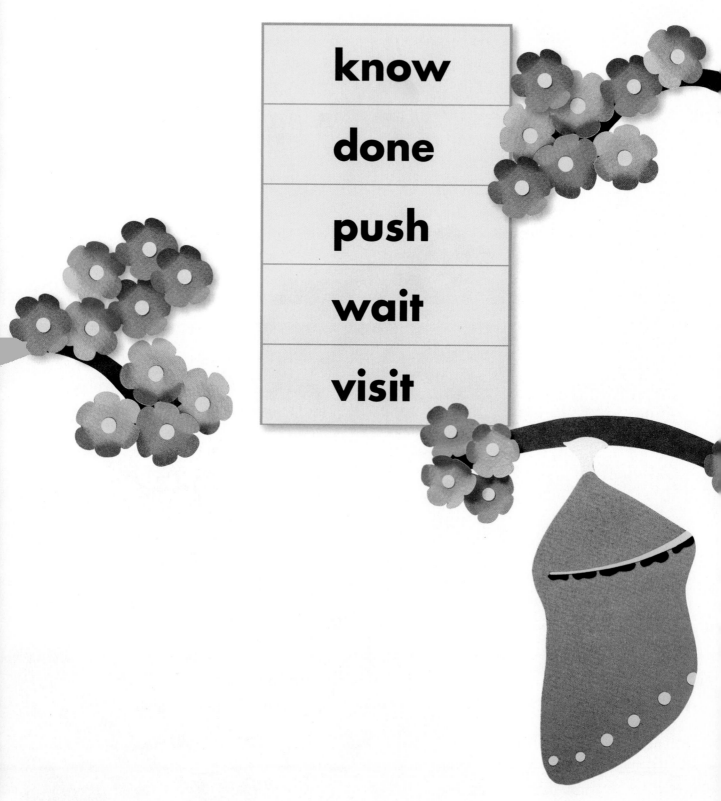

# Read the Words

Let's find out about insects.

Do you know what's in here?

When the insect inside is done growing, it will push its way out.

What will it be?
Wait and see.
Then it will visit the garden.

**Genre: Nonfiction**
Nonfiction selections teach us about something in the real world. Next you will read about the life cycle of a caterpillar.

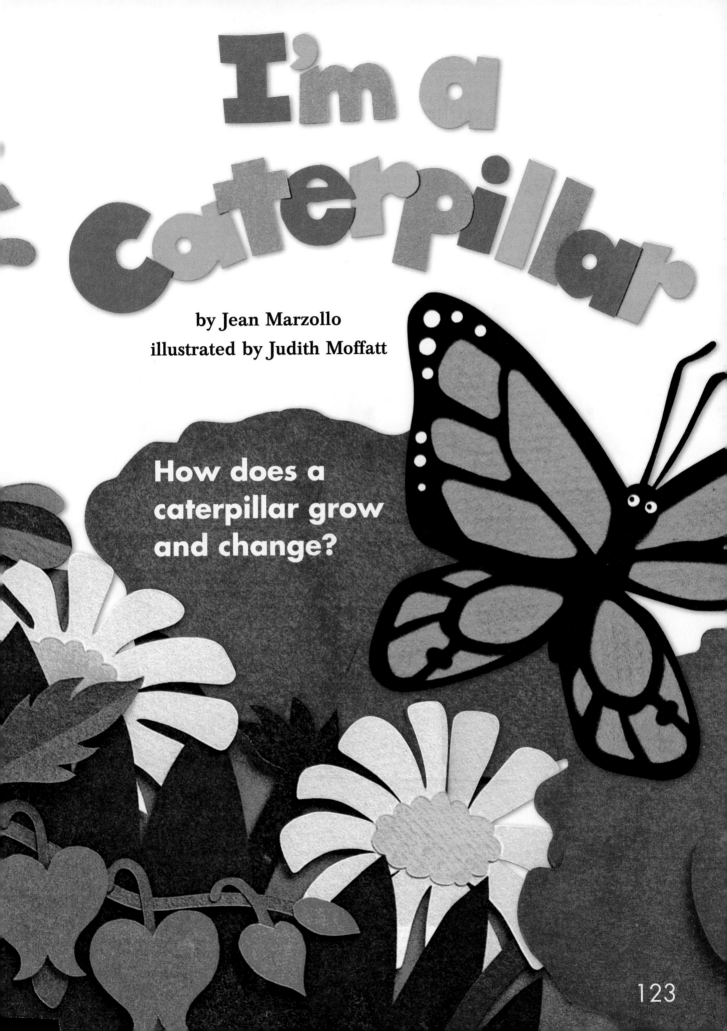

# I'm a Caterpillar

by Jean Marzollo
illustrated by Judith Moffatt

How does a
caterpillar grow
and change?

123

I'm a caterpillar. Munch. Crunch.
I'm getting bigger! Munch. Crunch.

Munch. Crunch. Munch. Crunch.

That's it. No more food. I'm done.

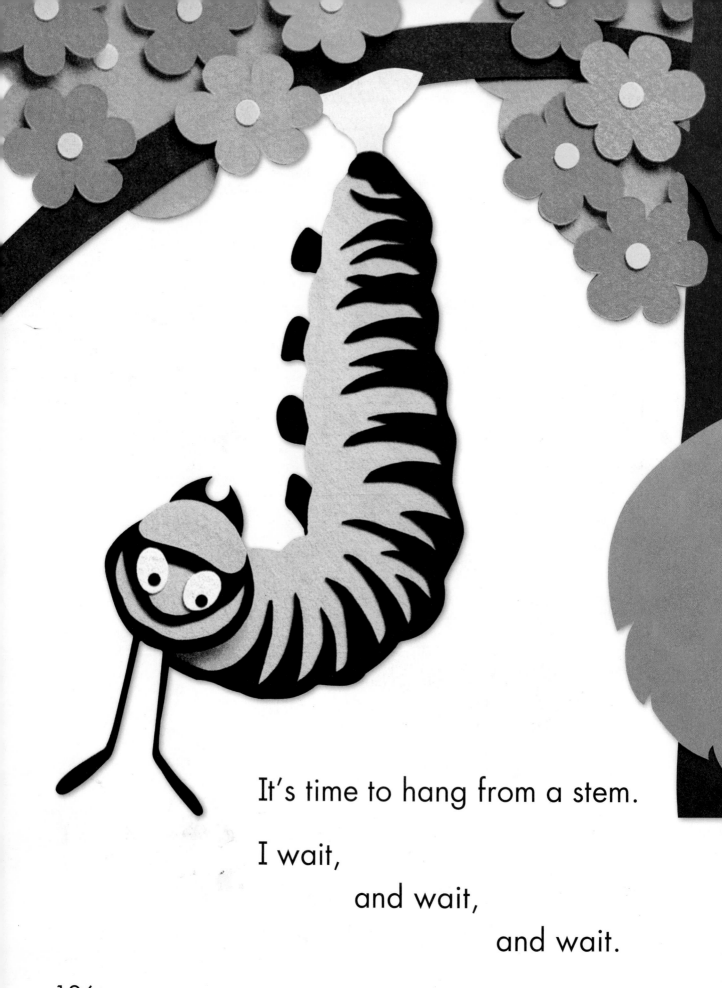

It's time to hang from a stem.

I wait,
    and wait,
        and wait.

126

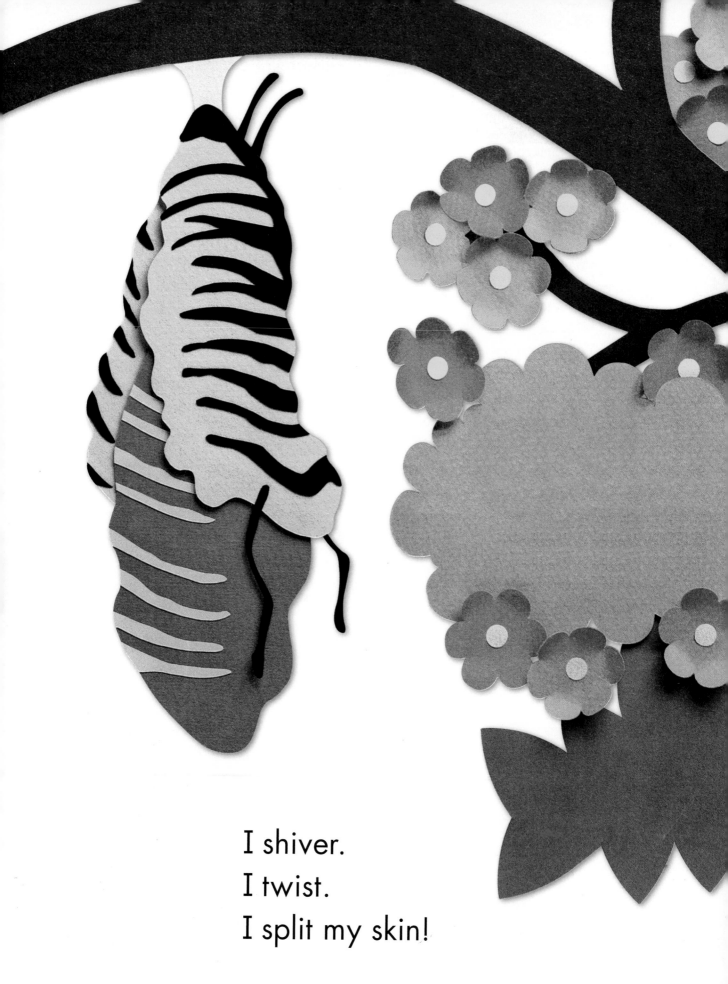

I shiver.
I twist.
I split my skin!

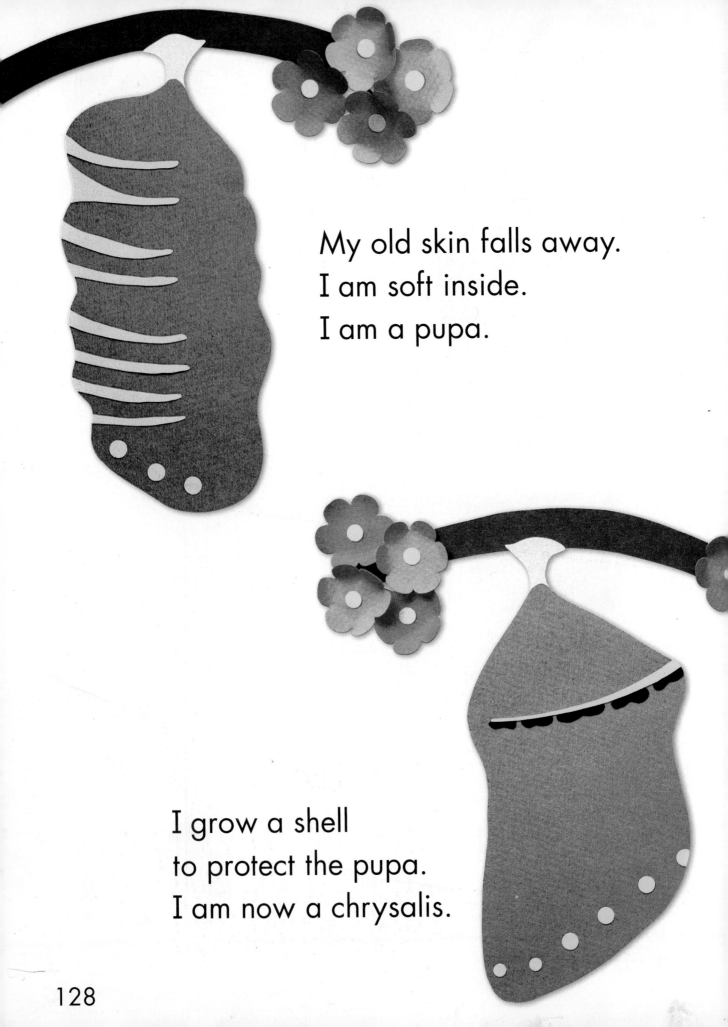

My old skin falls away.
I am soft inside.
I am a pupa.

I grow a shell
to protect the pupa.
I am now a chrysalis.

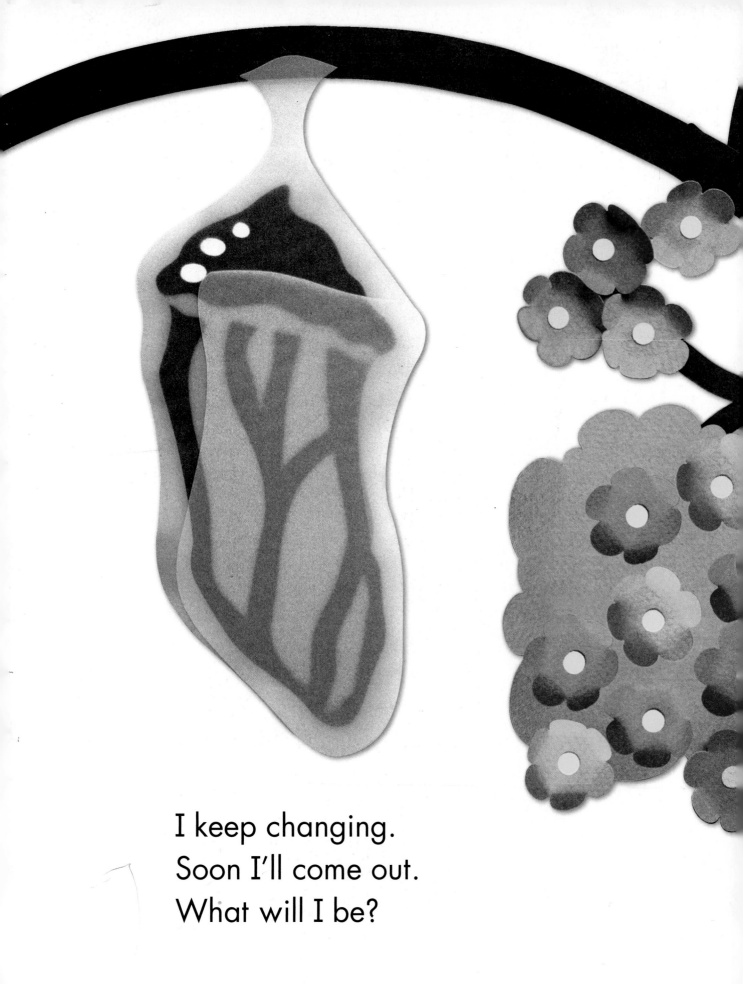

I keep changing.
Soon I'll come out.
What will I be?

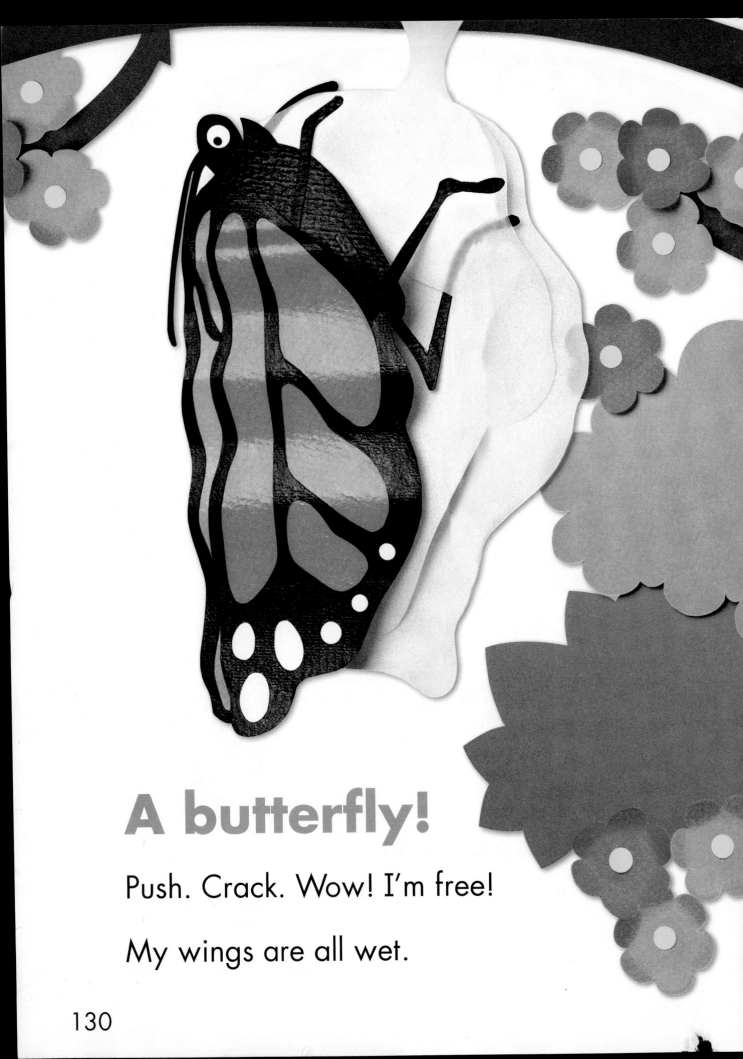

# A butterfly!

Push. Crack. Wow! I'm free!

My wings are all wet.

My wings dry off. They unfold.

Flap. Flap. Hey! I can fly! Ta-da!

I visit flowers. I drink nectar. Yum!

My mouth is like a straw.

Sip. Sip. Sip.

I have a mate. We visit many flowers.
We're not afraid of birds.
They know that we taste awful.

Soon I will lay my eggs.

The eggs have thin shells.

Baby caterpillars crawl out.

Hi! I'm a caterpillar.

Munch. Crunch.

**What will happen to me next?
Do you know?**

caterpillar

chrysalis

eggs

butterfly

# Think and Share

**Talk About It** What is one thing you learned about caterpillars? Tell about it.

**1.** Use the pictures below to summarize what you learned. Retell

**2.** Why do caterpillars eat so much?
Draw Conclusions

**3.** The writer tells about caterpillars from little to big or from caterpillar to butterfly. How did that order help you read and understand the story? Text Structure

**Look Back and Write** Look back at page 134. Why aren't butterflies afraid of birds?

## Meet the Author
# Jean Marzollo

Jean Marzollo was a high school teacher and a magazine editor. Now she has written more than 100 books for children! She writes about science, and she writes poetry, made-up stories, and *I Spy* books.

Ms. Marzollo likes to sew and work in her garden. She says writing is creative in the same way. It is hard and fun.

**Read other books by Jean Marzollo.**

# My Computer

Cursor

Keyboard

For more practice

Take It to the Net

PearsonSuccessNet.com

141

## Writing and Grammar

## Facts

### Prompt

In *I'm a Caterpillar,* a caterpillar changes into a butterfly. Think about these two insects. Now write facts about how the caterpillar looked before and how the butterfly looks now.

**Writing Trait**

All sentences should **focus** on the main **idea.**

**Student Model**

Writer describes each insect.

Adjectives give pictures of insects.

Sentences <u>focus</u> on how insects look.

The caterpillar was long and fat. Its legs were short and black.

The butterfly is colorful. Its wings are orange and black.

GEORGIA • Writing

GEORGIA Writing

For weekly writing in CRCT format, see the
*Georgia Weekly CRCT Workbook*, pages 109–112.

## Writer's Checklist

✓ **Ideas** Do all facts tell about the two insects?

✓ **Organization** Are ideas in order?

✓ **Style** Do adjectives tell about the insects?

✓ **Conventions** Are the right verbs used to tell about one and more than one?

# Grammar

## Am, Is, Are, Was, and Were

The words **am, is,** and **are** tell about now. Use **am** to tell about yourself. Use **is** to tell about one. Use **are** to tell about more than one.

The words **was** and **were** tell about the past. Use **was** to tell about one. Use **were** to tell about more than one.

· · · · · · · · · · · · · · · · · · · · · · · · · · · · · · · · · · · · · ·

Look at the facts. Write each verb. Does it tell about one or more than one?

**GEORGIA**

**Performance Standards** **ELA1W1e.** Writes in complete sentences with correct subject-verb agreement. (Also **ELA1W1a.**)

143

# Let's Talk About
# Changes in Nature

# Words to Read

| does |
| good-bye |
| before |
| won't |
| oh |
| right |

# Read the Words

"Does anyone know where Squirrel is?" asked Bear. "I want to say good-bye before my long nap. I won't see anyone for a while. Oh, I'm so sleepy! It is nap time right now."

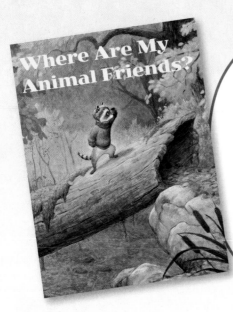

**Genre: Play**

A play is a story that is written to be acted out. Next you can read and then act out a play about animal friends who get ready for winter.

# Where Are My Animal Friends?

by William Chin
illustrated by Scott Gustafson

**Where do animals go when the days turn cold?**

# Characters

**Raccoon**

**Goose**

**Bear**

**Hummingbird**

**Squirrel**

Hello, Goose! Why are you shivering?

The forest is chilly, Raccoon. The days are shorter now. And it's getting colder every day.

Then we don't have much time to find our friends.

You're right, Raccoon. Let's look for Caterpillar.

Caterpillar lives in this tree.
But where are all the leaves?

Many of them are on the ground.
Where is Caterpillar?

152

Look, here comes the smallest bird in the forest. Hello, Hummingbird! Have you seen Caterpillar?

153

Oh, yes. Caterpillar is right here.

That's not Caterpillar! Caterpillar is long. This thing is not long.

Our friend Caterpillar moves a lot. This thing does not move at all.

But Caterpillar is inside. He became a chrysalis.

Then we won't see Caterpillar until spring when he'll be a butterfly.

Well, I'm glad you will be here for the winter.

 Oh, no, Raccoon. I can't stay. I must fly away to where it is warm. Hummingbird does too.

 Yes, we must go now.

Oh, my! I am the saddest raccoon in the forest. Will you come back?

Yes, we'll be back in the spring. Good-bye, Raccoon!

Good-bye, Goose! Good-bye, Hummingbird! I will see if Bear is at home.

Hello, Bear!

 Hello, Raccoon. Is it spring yet?

 No, Bear. It will be winter before it is spring. Why are you sleeping?

 I ate and ate all summer. Now I am fatter than before, and I don't need to eat. I will sleep a long time. I won't budge until spring.

Oh, no! All my friends
are going away!

 Pardon me, but I'm sleepy.
Good night, Raccoon!

159

Good night, Bear. But who will be my friend? Oh, here comes Squirrel.

Hello, Raccoon. Where is everyone?

Goose flew away, and so did Hummingbird. Caterpillar is now a chrysalis, and Bear is sleeping for the winter. Are you going away too?

Oh, no. I will stay here all winter.
I have a warm nest and lots of food.
Will you play with me?

Yes, Squirrel! Let's race to the edge of the forest and back!

# Put on a Play!

What you will need:

## Costumes

Costumes can be simple or fancy.

## Props

One prop you will
need for this play is
a chrysalis. Will you
need anything else?

# Scenery

Simple sets can show that the play
is set in a forest in the fall.

# An Audience

Practice your parts. Then ask another
class to come to the play!

# Think and Share

**Talk About It** Only one of Raccoon's friends will stay for the winter. What do you think they will do together all winter long?

**1.** Use the pictures below to retell the story.
**Retell**

**2.** What does Bear do before he goes to sleep for the winter? **Sequence**

**3.** What did you know about caterpillars that helped as you read? **Prior Knowledge**

**Look Back and Write** Look back at pages 151 and 152. How do the animals know that winter is coming to the forest?

# William Chin

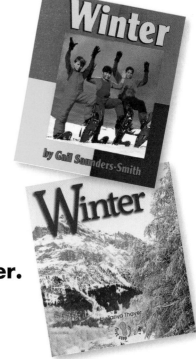

William Chin likes the winter. He lives in Chicago, where it gets cold in winter. His daughter is a figure skater. He and his wife skate too.

Mr. Chin sang in musicals in school. Now he is a choir director. He works with a children's choir. He is also a conductor for the Chicago Symphony Chorus.

**Here are more books about winter.**

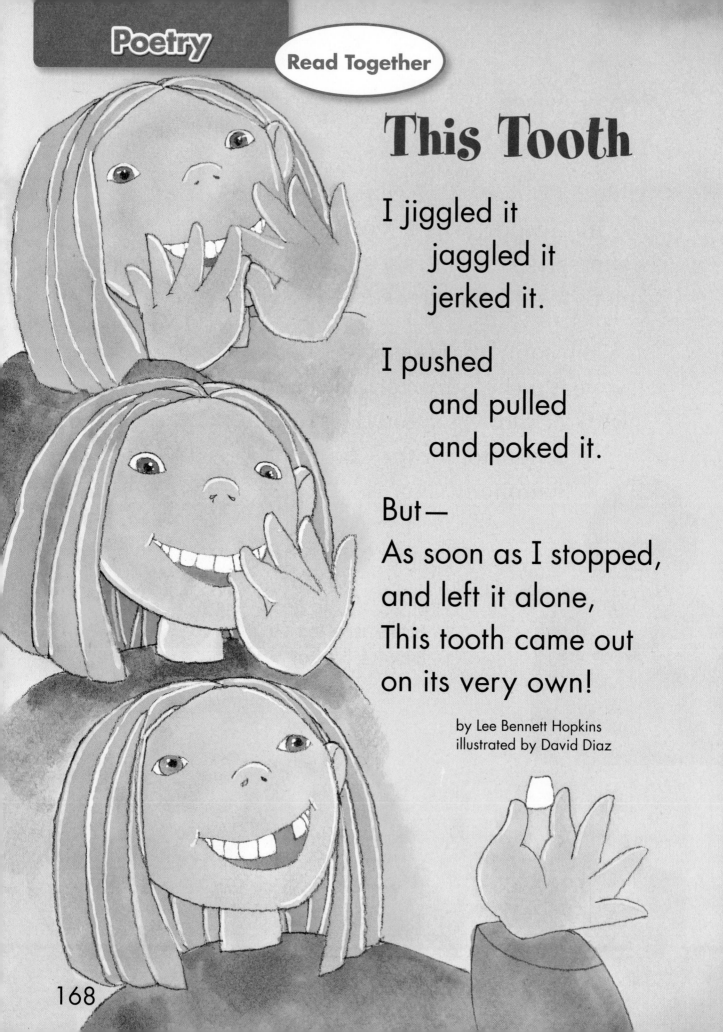

# This Tooth

I jiggled it
    jaggled it
      jerked it.

I pushed
    and pulled
      and poked it.

But—

As soon as I stopped,
and left it alone,
This tooth came out
on its very own!

by Lee Bennett Hopkins
illustrated by David Diaz

# Tommy

I put a seed into the ground
And said, "I'll watch it grow."
I watered it and cared for it
As well as I could know.

One day I walked in my back yard,
and oh, what did I see!
My seed had popped itself right out,
Without consulting me.

by Gwendolyn Brooks
illustrated by David Diaz

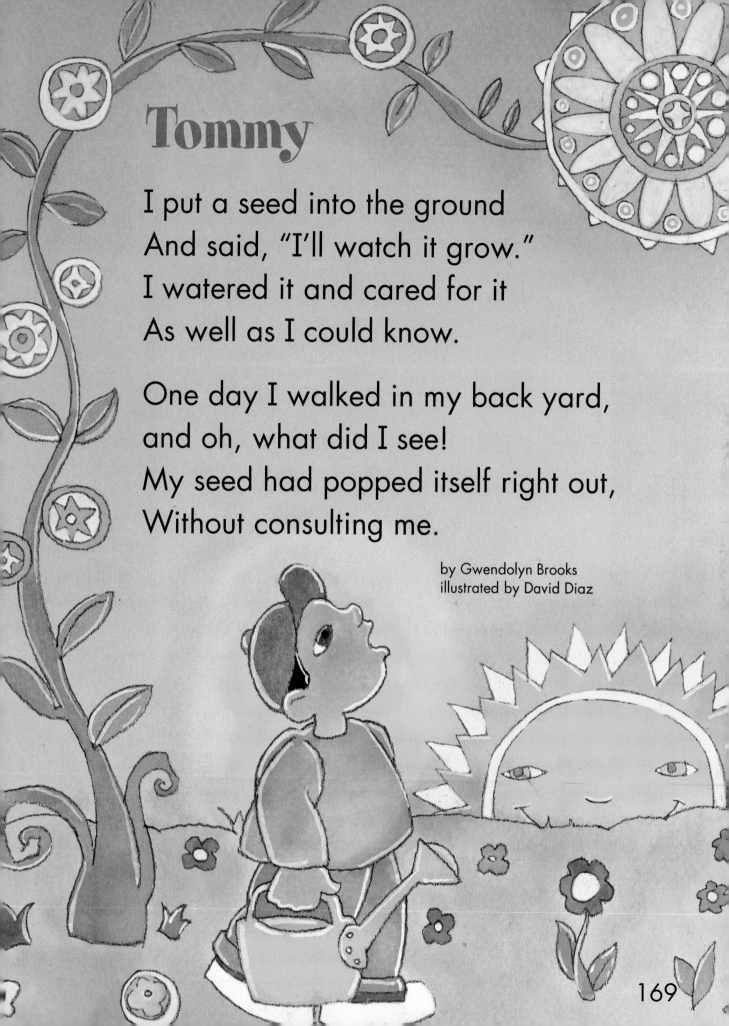

# Where Do Fish Go in Winter?

When lakes turn to ice
And are covered with snow,
What becomes of the fish
Who are living below?

It's not so exciting
Down under the ice,
But fish find it restful
And really quite nice.

It's dark and it's cold,
But the water's not frozen.
In fact, it's just perfect
For fish to repose in.

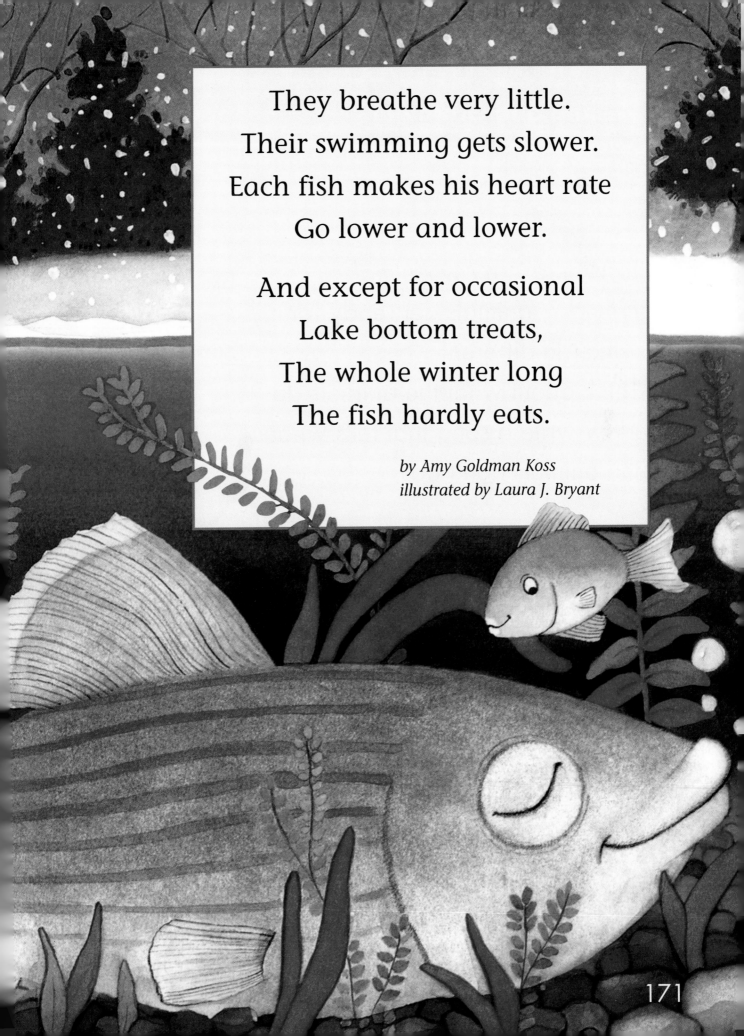

They breathe very little.
Their swimming gets slower.
Each fish makes his heart rate
Go lower and lower.

And except for occasional
Lake bottom treats,
The whole winter long
The fish hardly eats.

*by Amy Goldman Koss*
*illustrated by Laura J. Bryant*

# Write Now

**Writing and Grammar**

## Song

### Prompt

In *Where Are My Animal Friends?*, animals get ready for winter in different ways. Think about what the animals do. Now write a song that tells what the animals <u>don't</u> do.

**Writing Trait**

Like a story, a song can have **sentences.**

**Student Model**

**Song names three animals.**

**Rhyming words are at the end of lines.**

<u>Sentences</u> in song end with periods.

### In Winter

Caterpillars don't fly away.
A bear doesn't work all day.
Robins aren't here to stay.

172

GEORGIA • Writing

**GEORGIA Writing**
For weekly writing in CRCT format, see the
*Georgia Weekly CRCT Workbook*, pages 117–120.

## Writer's Checklist

✓ **Ideas** Does the song follow the prompt?

✓ **Organization** Does word order make sense?

✓ **Style** Does the song have rhyming words?

✓ **Conventions** Do sentences begin with capital letters?

# Grammar

## Contractions with Not

A **contraction** is a short way to put two words together. A **verb** and the word **not** can make a contraction. An **apostrophe (')** is used in place of the letter **o** in **not.**

are + not = **aren't**          do + not = **don't**

has + not = **hasn't**       does + not = **doesn't**

. . . . . . . . . . . . . . . . . . . . . . . . . . . . . . .

Write the contractions in the song. Write two words that make each contraction.

**GEORGIA**
**Performance Standards**   **ELA1W1a.** Writes texts of a length appropriate to address a topic and tell a story. (Also
**GPS**   **ELA1W1e.**)

173

# Wrap-Up

## Growing Me

connect to
**WRITING**

How have you changed since you began first grade? Make a picture. Show one way you changed. Write a sentence about it.

I am taller.

## How Seeds Grow and Change

connect to
**SCIENCE**

Plant some seeds. Radish seeds or grass seeds are good. Water the seeds. Then put them in the sun. Watch them for a few days. Make a picture. Show what happens. Write what the seeds need to grow.

## Step by Step

connect to
**SCIENCE**

Make a caterpillar from five big paper circles. Think about how a caterpillar grows. Show one step on each circle.

175

# Glossary

## Bb

boy

**beautiful** If something is **beautiful,** it is very pretty to see or hear. After the rain stopped, it became a **beautiful,** sunny day.

**boy** A **boy** is a male child. A **boy** grows up to be a man.

## Cc

**caterpillar** A **caterpillar** is an insect that looks like a furry worm. **Caterpillars** turn into moths or butterflies.

caterpillar

176

**chrysalis**  A caterpillar becomes a **chrysalis** when it grows a hard shell around itself.

chrysalis

**crawl**  When you **crawl**, you move on your hands and knees or with your body close to the ground. Worms, snakes, and lizards **crawl.**

## Ff

**father**  A **father** is a man who has a child or children.

**feather**  A **feather** is one of the light, soft things that cover a bird's body.

feather

**flew**  The bird **flew** away. We **flew** to New York in an airplane.

## Gg

**goose** A **goose** is a large bird with a long neck. A **goose** looks like a duck but is larger.

goose

**grew** The grass **grew** very fast from all the rain.

**ground** The **ground** is the soil or dirt on the surface of the Earth. The **ground** was rocky.

## Hh

**head** Your **head** is the top part of your body or the front part of most animals' bodies. Your **head** is where your eyes, ears, nose, mouth, and brain are.

head

## Mm

**mother**  A **mother** is a woman who has a child or children.

mother

**move**  To **move** means to change the place where you live. We live in the city now, but my parents want to **move** to the country.

## Nn

**night**  **Night** is the time between evening and morning.

night

## Pp

**precious** **Precious** means having great value. Mom's ring is very **precious** to her.

precious

**pupa** The **pupa** is the form of an insect while it is changing from a wormlike larva into an adult.

## Rr

raccoon

**raccoon** A **raccoon** is a small animal with thick fur. Its tail is long and has rings of a different color. **Raccoons** look for food at night.

rain

**rain** **Rain** is the water that falls in drops from the clouds. The **rain** made us all wet as we walked home from school.

**Ss**

**shiver** To **shiver** is to shake.

**shouted** When you have **shouted,** you have called out or yelled loudly. She **shouted** for help.

**shouting** When you are **shouting,** you are calling or yelling.

shouting

**spring** **Spring** is the season of the year between winter and summer. **Spring** is the season when plants begin to grow.

**sunset** **Sunset** is the time when the sun is last seen in the evening.

sunset

181

**Tt**

**tower** A **tower** is a tall building or part of a building. A **tower** may stand alone or may be a part of a church, castle, or other building.

tower

**toys** **Toys** are things to play with. Dolls, blocks, and teddy bears are **toys.**

toys

# Ww

**warm** If something is **warm,** it is more hot than cold. The water is **warm** enough to swim in. He sat in the **warm** sunshine.

**window** A **window** is an opening in a wall or roof. A **window** lets in light or fresh air.

window

# Tested Words

### An Egg Is an Egg

always
become
day
everything
nothing
stays
things

### Ruby in Her Own Time

any
enough
ever
every
own
sure
were

## Jan's New Home

away
car
friends
house
our
school
very

## Frog and Toad Together

afraid
again
few
how
read
soon

# Tested Words

## I'm a Caterpillar

done
know
push
visit
wait

## Where Are My Animal Friends?

before
does
good-bye
oh
right
won't

# Acknowledgments

## Text

**Page 14:** From *An Egg Is an Egg* by Nicki Weiss, copyright © 1990 by Monica J. Weiss. Used by permission G.P. Putnam's Sons, A Division of Penguin Young Readers Group, A Member of Penguin Group (USA) Inc., 345 Hudson Street, New York, NY 10014. All rights reserved.

**Page 40:** *Ruby in Her Own Time* by Jonathan Emmett, illustrated by Rebecca Horry. Text copyright © 2003 by Jonathan Emmett, illustration copyright © 2003 by Rebecca Harry. Reprinted by permission of Scholastic Inc.

**Page 96:** "The Garden" from *Frog and Toad Together* by Arnold Lobel. Used by permission of HarperCollins Publishers.

**Page 122:** From *I'm A Caterpillar* by Jean Marzollo, illustrated by Judith Moffat. A Hello Science Reader! Book published by Cartwheel Books/Scholastic Inc. Text copyright © 1997 by Jean Marzollo, illustrations copyright © 1997 by Judith Moffat. Reprinted by permission. Hello Reader and Cartwheel Books are registered trademarks of Scholastic Inc.

**Page 168:** "This Tooth" by Lee Bennett Hopkins. Copyright © 1970 by Lee Bennett Hopkins. First appeared in *ME!*, published by Seabury Press. Reprinted by permission of Curtis Brown, Ltd.

Page 169: "Tommy" by Gwendolyn Brooks. Reprinted by consent of Brooks Permission.

**Page 170:** "Where Do Fish Go In Winter?", from *Where fish Go in Winter And Other great Mysteries* by Amy Goldman Koss, copyright © 1987, by Amy Goldman Koss, text. Illustrated by Laura J. Bryant, copyright © 2002 by Laura J. Bryant, illustrations. Used by permission of Dial Books for Young Readers, A Division of Penguin Young Readers Group, A Member of Penguin Group (USA) Inc., 345 Hudson Street, New York, NY 10014. All rights reserved.

## Illustrations

**Cover:** Daniel Moreton

**11-27, 34-35, 174-175** Julia Woolf; **30-33** Mary Bono; **68** Steven Mach; **69-85, 90-91** Don Tate; **145-163, 173** Scott Gustafson; **164-165** Courtesy David Diaz

## Photographs

Every effort has been made to secure permission and provide appropriate credit for photographic material. The publisher deeply regrets any omission and pledges to correct errors called to its attention in subsequent editions.

Unless otherwise acknowledged, all photographs are the property of Scott Foresman, a division of Pearson Education.

Photo locators denoted as follows: Top (T), Center (C), Bottom (B), Left (L), Right (R), Background (Bkgd).

**8** ©Michael & Patricia Fogden/Corbis, (Bkgd) ©Clay Perry/Corbis

**10** ©Ariel Skelley/Corbis

**11** (T) ©Kevin Dodge/Masterfile Corporation, (BL) ©Michael Newman/PhotoEdit

**29** ©Nicki Weiss

**36** (BC) Digital Vision, (BL) ©Jim Craigmyle/Corbis, (BR) ©Tom & Dee Ann McCarthy/Corbis

**37** (BL) ©Royalty-Free/Corbis, (BR) ©Janette Beckman/Corbis

**64** (CR, CL) ©Ariel Skelley/Corbis

**69** (CL) Getty Images, (TR) Tom & Dee Ann McCarthy/Corbis

**92** ©Frank Cruz/Index Stock Imagery

**93** (TL) ©Ben Weaver/Getty Images, (CR) ©Roger Ball/Corbis

**114** Dave King/©DK Images

**115** (CL) ©D. Boone/Corbis, (BL) ©William Taufic/Corbis

**118** (CC) ©John Isaac/Getty Images, (CL, BC, CR) ©DK Images

**119** (TL, TR, CC) ©DK Images, (TC) Frank Greenaway/©DK Images

**121** (TR) ©John Mason (JLMO)/Ardea, (CC) ©Richard Cummins/Corbis

**144** ©Ted Horowitz/Corbis

**145** (T) ©LWA-Dann Tardif/Corbis, (C) ©James L. Amos/Corbis, (B) ©Carol Fuegi/Corbis

**176** (TL) Rubberball Productions, (B) Digital Vision

**177** (TR) Getty Images, (BL) Hemera Technologies

**178** Hemera Technologies

**179** (BC) Getty Images, (TR) Rubberball Productions

**180** (TR) Hemera Technologies, (CR) ©Royalty-Free/Corbis, (BL) Ghislain & Marie David de Lossy/Image Bank/Getty Images

**182** (L, CC, CL) Hemera Technologies, (CR, TR) Getty Images

**183** (C) Getty Images

## Glossary

The contents of this glossary have been adapted from *First Dictionary.* Copyright © 2000, Pearson Education, Inc.